CHART H...S

DOWNLOAD TO YOUR COMPUTER A SET OF PIANO ACCOMPANIMENTS FOR
THIS EDITION (TO BE PLAYED BY A TEACHER/PARENT/FRIEND).
VISIT: WWW.HYBRIDPUBLICATIONS.COM REGISTRATION IS FREE AND EASY.
YOUR REGISTRATION CODE IS KF543.

PUBLISHED BY
WISE PUBLICATIONS
14-15 BERNERS STREET, LONDON, W1T 3LJ, UK.

EXCLUSIVE DISTRIBUTORS:
MUSIC SALES LIMITED
DISTRIBUTION CENTRE, NEWMARKET ROAD, BURY ST EDMUNDS,
SUFFOLK, IP33 3YB, UK.
MUSIC SALES PTY LIMITED
20 RESOLUTION DRIVE, CARINGBAH, NSW 2229, AUSTRALIA.

ORDER NO. AM1000054
ISBN 978-1-84938-477-3
THIS BOOK © COPYRIGHT 2010 BY WISE PUBLICATIONS,
A DIVISION OF MUSIC SALES LIMITED.

EDITED BY OLIVER MILLER.
MUSIC ARRANGED BY PAUL HONEY.
MUSIC PROCESSED BY PAUL EWERS MUSIC DESIGN.

BACKING TRACKS:
HOWARD McGILL – FLUTE
PAUL HONEY – PIANO

PRINTED IN THE EU.

YOUR GUARANTEE OF QUALITY
AS PUBLISHERS, WE STRIVE TO PRODUCE EVERY BOOK TO THE HIGHEST
COMMERCIAL STANDARDS. THE MUSIC HAS BEEN FRESHLY ENGRAVED AND
THE BOOK HAS BEEN CAREFULLY DESIGNED TO MINIMISE AWKWARD PAGE
TURNS AND TO MAKE PLAYING FROM IT A REAL PLEASURE.
PARTICULAR CARE HAS BEEN GIVEN TO SPECIFYING ACID-FREE, NEUTRAL-
SIZED PAPER MADE FROM PULPS WHICH HAVE NOT BEEN ELEMENTAL
CHLORINE BLEACHED. THIS PULP IS FROM FARMED SUSTAINABLE FORESTS
AND WAS PRODUCED WITH SPECIAL REGARD FOR THE ENVIRONMENT.
THROUGHOUT, THE PRINTING AND BINDING HAVE BEEN PLANNED TO
ENSURE A STURDY, ATTRACTIVE PUBLICATION WHICH SHOULD GIVE YEARS
OF ENJOYMENT. IF YOUR COPY FAILS TO MEET OUR HIGH STANDARDS,
PLEASE INFORM US AND WE WILL GLADLY REPLACE IT.

WWW.MUSICSALES.COM

WISE PUBLICATIONS
PART OF THE MUSIC SALES GROUP
LONDON / NEW YORK / PARIS / SYDNEY / COPENHAGEN / BERLIN / MADRID / HONG KONG / TOKYO

U2
Beautiful Day

Words by Bono • Music by U2

The lead single from U2's album, *All That You Can't Leave Behind*, this optimistic anthem, about a man who has lost everything but nevertheless can find joy in what he still has, won three Grammy Awards in 2001. It became the veteran Irish rock band's fourth UK No. 1 single since their emergence in the early 1980s.

Hints & Tips: This melody contains some large intervals and regular intervals of a 5th or 6th. The lips need to learn to cope with large intervals and can only do that with slow and careful practice.

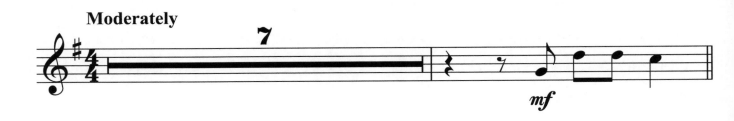

LEONA LEWIS

Bleeding Love

Words & Music by Ryan Tedder & Jesse McCartney

This was the biggest selling UK single of 2007, recorded by the winner of the third series of TV talent show The X Factor and Hello! magazine's 2007 Woman of the Year. It was No. 1 in the UK Singles Chart for six weeks and is included on Leona Lewis's debut album *Spirit*, the fastest-selling debut album in the UK ever.

Hints & Tips: This is a good exercise for the notes of the lower register. Remember to keep your right-hand little finger on it's key, but lift it for the D in bar 25.

JAMES MORRISON FEAT. NELLY FURTADO

Broken Strings

Words & Music by James Morrison, Nina Woodford & Fraser Thorneycroft-Smith

This mid-tempo ballad from Morrison's second studio album *Songs For You, Truths for Me,* about the struggle at the close of a relationship that is beyond repair, became his most successful single to date. It broke into the UK Top 10 following his live performance of the song on UK TV with Girls Aloud.

Hints & Tips: It is useful to practise scales in the same key as a piece you are learning, helping the fingers to become familiar with the correct patterns; for this song in D major it would also be useful to practise arpeggios. In keeping with the feel of the music, produce a gentle, warm tone.

Moderately

Chasing Cars

Words & Music by Gary Lightbody, Nathan Connolly, Jonathan Quinn, Paul Wilson & Tom Simpson

The longevity of this CD single in the UK charts illustrates the impact of legal downloads because, although it peaked at No. 6, it has spent at least 130 weeks in the Top 100, despite a physical copy being available for only 14 of them. Its popularity in the US came after it featured on the TV medical drama Grey's Anatomy.

Hints & Tips: Songs are usually reliant on both their words and the music to express their full meaning. When playing an instrument we use articulation and dynamics to help express the music. For this song play the written dynamics to add effect and expression, particularly by playing quite softly up to bar 18 where it becomes loud.

Fix You

Words & Music by Guy Berryman, Chris Martin, Jon Buckland & Will Champion

When released as an EP on iTunes Music Store in September 2005 all sales went to the American Red Cross Hurricane 2005 Relief and the National Academy of Recording Arts & Sciences' MusiCare Hurricane Relief Fund. It became a tribute song for victims of the disaster, although it is also said to have been written by Chris Martin for his wife Gwyneth Paltrow, to comfort her after the death of her father.

Hints & Tips: Don't let the upbeats catch you out, be ready for them by breathing a couple of beats early and have your instrument ready to play the first note.

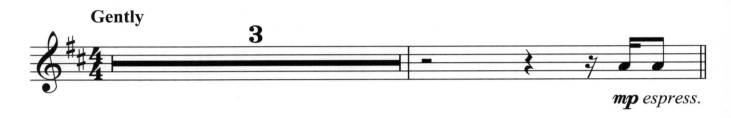

ALEXANDRA BURKE

Hallelujah

Words & Music by Leonard Cohen

Released in December 2008, this X Factor-winning version of Leonard Cohen's 1984 biblical epic, condensed from its original 80 verses, broke the European record for single sales over 24 hours and was the UK's top-selling single of the year as well as claiming the coveted Christmas No. 1 spot.

Hints & Tips: It is useful and sometimes essential to silently count the beat, especially when playing in an ensemble, when you are not always playing. This song is in the compound time signature of $\frac{6}{8}$, which when it moves fast can be counted in 2 rather than two groups of 3, this way the music will sway and have style.

If I Were A Boy

Words & Music by Tobias Gad & Britney Carlson

Inspired by the smell of pizza being sold in Times Square, New York, BC Jean wrote this emotive tome of torment within minutes of returning to her studio. The original version was rejected by her record company but its potential was recognised by Beyoncé, for whom it became a fourth UK No. 1 single in November 2008.

Hints & Tips: At bar 18, when the melody ascends to the middle and upper registers, use more support from the airstream by speeding it up. This song is in F major and doesn't change key or revert to B♮ at all, so for ease of playing use the B♭ thumb key, rather than the regular B thumb key, throughout.

To Coda ⊕

mp

D.S. al Coda

f

⊕ **Coda**

mp

Just Dance

Words & Music by Aliaune Thiam, Stefani Germanotta & Nadir Khayat

This booming fusion of electro-pop and R&B was a No. 1 hit in many countries on both sides of the Atlantic. In the UK it was the first new No. 1 single of 2009, whilst in the USA, after debuting at No. 76 in August 2008, it took 22 weeks to reach the summit of the Billboard Hot 100; the second-longest climb ever.

Hints & Tips: Because there are not many long rests in which to breathe, take every sensible opportunity to snatch breaths in the shorter rests. From bar 33 pay careful attention to rhythm, otherwise there is a risk of getting out of sync with the backing track.

Leave Right Now

Words & Music by Eg White

According to Will Young, winner of the first UK Pop Idol competition, this is 'a classically sad song about what your heart and your head says'. This was Young's fourth UK No. 1 single and the first to be taken from his second album, *Friday's Child*. It won the 2004 Ivor Novello Award for Best Song, Musically and Lyrically, for composer Francis 'Eg' White.

Hints & Tips: Be neat when tonguing the semiquaver passages throughout this song; take big breaths in advance and support these passages with the airstream. Take care that you don't let too much air escape, but instead, concentrate on making a good clear sound.

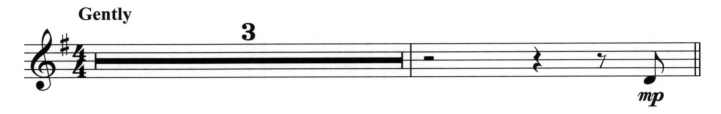

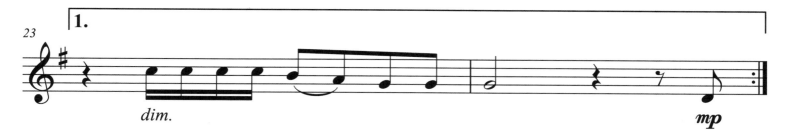

Love Song

Words & Music by Sara Bareilles

Having begun songwriting and performing whilst studying Communications at UCLA, Californian Sara Bareilles' relatively small following was quickly turned into national exposure when this song was selected as the free single of the week by iTunes in June 2007. It went on to reach No. 4 in both the UK and the USA.

Hints & Tips: The harmonies in this song are unusual and therefore the backing track could occasionally feel off-putting, as if it were incorrect. Offset this by ensuring you have confidently practised the notes correctly before playing with the backing track.

Moderate shuffle feel (swung ♪'s)

Shine

Words & Music by Mark Owen, Gary Barlow, Stephen Robson, Jason Orange & Howard Donald

Taken from their comeback album, *Beautiful World,* this song became Take That's sixth consecutive No. 1 and their tenth overall when it topped the UK charts in March 2007. It won the Ivor Novello award for Most Performed Work in 2007 and the 2008 Brit Award for Best British Single, the band winning Best Live Act.

Hints & Tips: The repeated staccato notes at the beginning should be separated but not too spiky, otherwise it could sound aggressive. Watch out for accidentals which are scattered throughout the song.

Take A Bow

Words & Music by Mikkel Eriksen, Tor Erik Hermansen & Shaffer Smith

This velvety piano ballad about a deceiving partner was written for the re-release of Rihanna's album *Good Girl Gone Bad* and became her third US No. 1 single by jumping 52 places to the top of the Billboard Hot 100. In the UK it debuted at No. 2 on downloads alone, rising to No. 1 the following week.

Hints & Tips: Prepare for the first note by holding your instrument correctly and have your embouchure ready to play an A. Practise the section from bar 27 to bar 29 with a metronome, to get the syncopated rhythm solid.

DUFFY
Warwick Avenue

Words & Music by Duffy, James Hogarth & Eg White

This laidback melodramatic slab of 1970s soul spent six weeks in the Top 10 of the UK Singles Chart. It was the third release from Welsh chanteuse Duffy's chart-topping debut album *Rockferry* for which she was awarded the 2009 Grammy Award for Best Pop Vocal Album.

Hints & Tips: Although the musical direction asks you to play lazily, don't be caught out by the $\frac{6}{8}$ bar at bar 30.

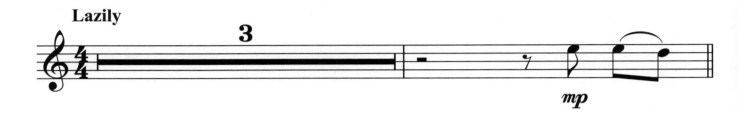

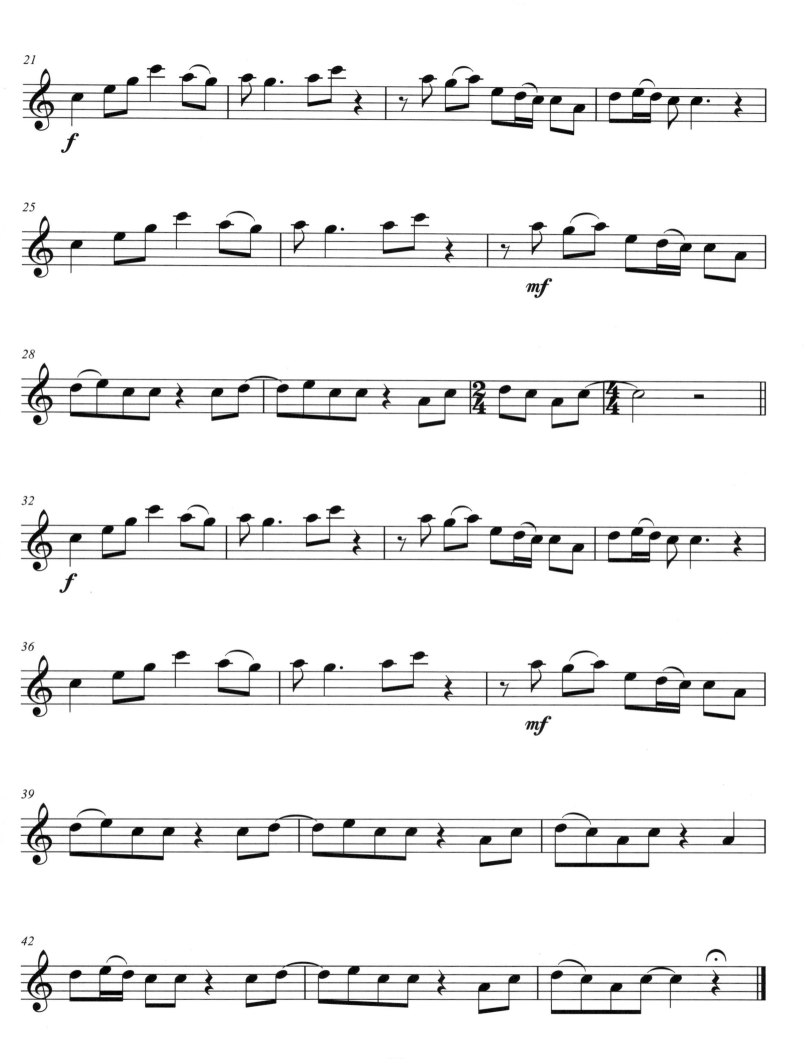

You Raise Me Up

Words & Music by Brendan Graham & Rolf Løvland

Only The Beatles, Elvis and Cliff Richard have had more No. 1 hit singles than Westlife's 18. In November 2005, after a gap of two years, this song, originally an instrumental called 'Silent Story' and recorded by Secret Garden on their album *Once In A Red Moon*, became their 13th. It and went on to become the UK Record of the Year.

Hints & Tips: Because of the repetitive nature of this song it will be most effective if it is played incorporating all the dynamics that are written.

Lost

Words & Music by Michael Bublé, Alan Chang & Jann Richards

Bublé described this emotive ballad, one of two self-penned originals on his third studio album *Call Me Irresponsible*, as 'an anthem for star-crossed lovers' and 'my remark on the state of love'. Inspired by the break-up with his former fiancée, Bublé's spine-tingling vocal range combines gentleness with powerful expression.

Hints & Tips: Keep the melody smooth and legato in this slow and gentle song. Pay particular attention to the ends of slurs, making sure that they don't finish too abruptly or are cut short.

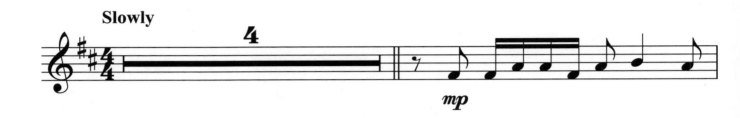